LOST IN A BOOK

Illustrated by Mark Walker

Devised by WildPixel

ARCTURUS

ARCTURUS

This edition published in 2019 by Arcturus Publishing Limited
26/27 Bickels Yard, 151–153 Bermondsey Street,
London SE1 3HA

Illustrated by Mark Walker
Written by Joanne Dearden
Designed by WildPixel Ltd.
Edited by Sebastian Rydberg

ISBN: 978-1-78888-477-8
CH006623NT
Supplier 29, Date 0319, Print run 8151

Printed in China

STEP INTO
LOST IN A BOOK

Turn the page to lose yourself in a wonderful compendium of stories,
craftily reimagined as ingenious puzzles.

Each maze represents a scene from a classic novel or fairy tale. These well-loved
stories—such as J. M. Barrie's *Peter Pan*, L. Frank Baum's *The Wonderful Wizard of Oz*,
and Lewis Carroll's *Alice's Adventures in Wonderland*—have found a special place in the
imagination of children and adults, far outlasting the lifetimes of their original authors.

After solving the mazes, why not revisit the classic tales and
read the stories that inspired this book?

Start

Encounter characters from books
and fairy tales along the way

Finish

Move from Start
to Finish

Start

Avoid dead ends and
blocked routes

Tip:
Some mazes (such as
Rapunzel on pages 8 and
9) run sideways across
the page so you will need
to give the open book
a quarter turn to solve
them.

And if you're stuck, you can always turn to **page 60** for the solutions.

Start

Alice's Adventures in Wonderland

"Curiouser and curiouser..." Alice is falling down the rabbit hole. Can you help her find the White Rabbit?

Finish

Sleeping Beauty

The Prince must find a way through the enchanted forest to rescue Sleeping Beauty. Watch out for prickly thorns and brambles!

Start

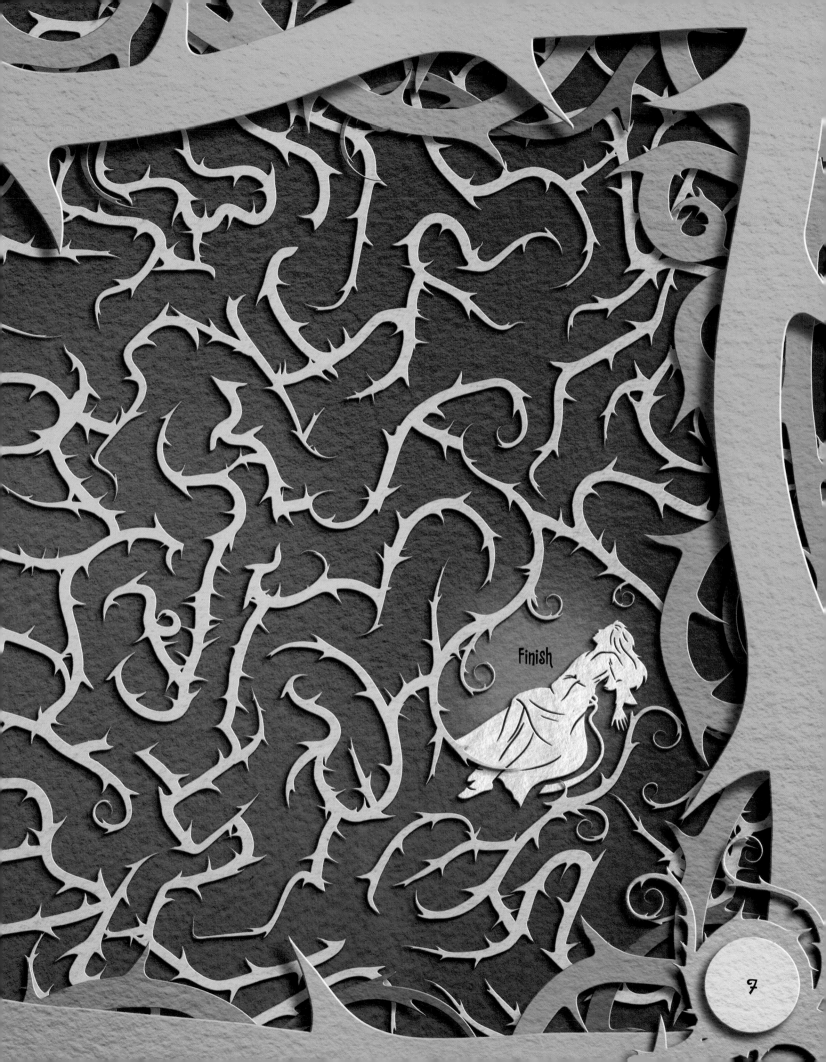

Finish

Finish

Rapunzel

Rapunzel has let down her hair. Which of the golden tresses should the Prince climb to reach the top of the tower?

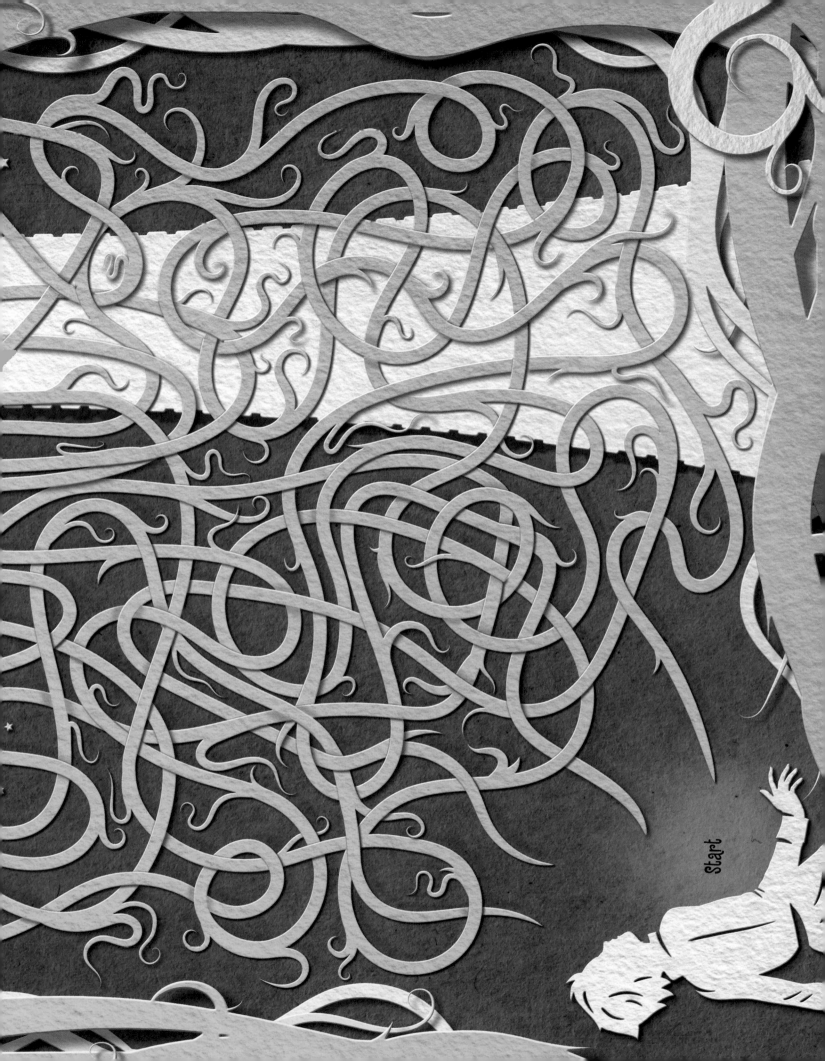

Treasure Island

"Fifteen men on a dead man's chest!" Long John Silver, Dr. Livesey, Squire Trelawney, and Jim the cabin boy have set sail. Guide their ship—the *Hispaniola*—through the channels to Treasure Island!

Start

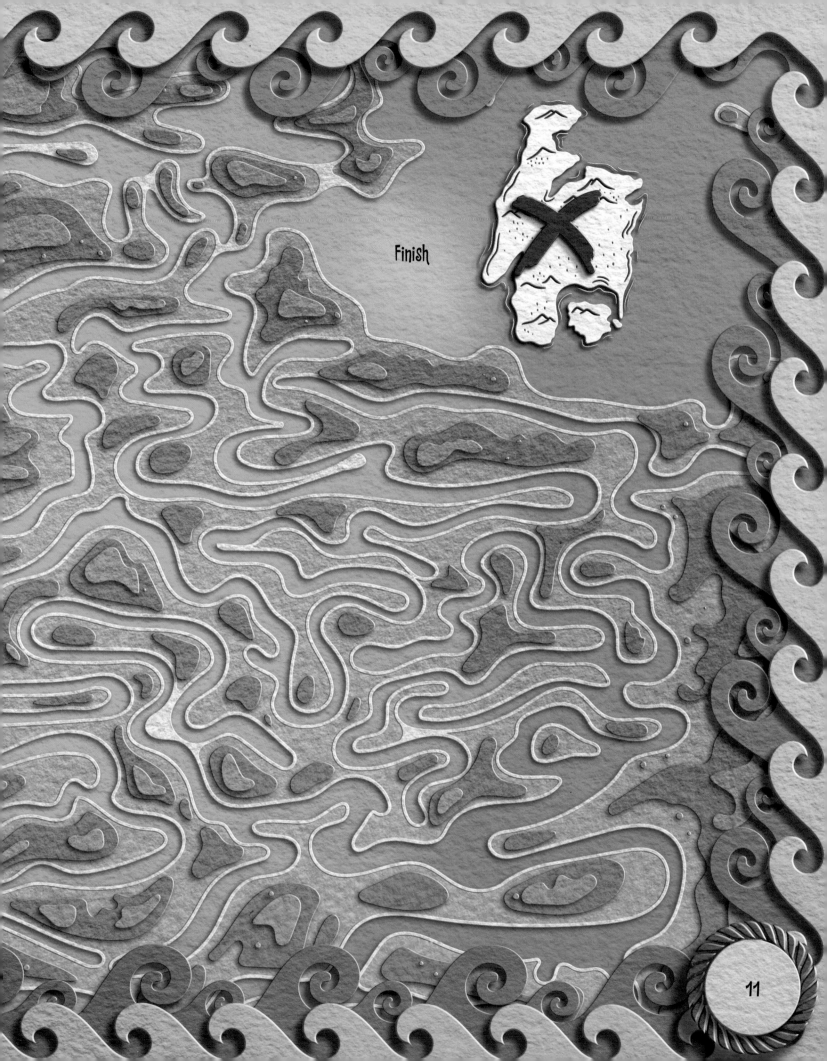

Finish

11

Hansel and Gretel

Hansel and Gretel are lost in the woods—can you help them find their way home and pick up the pebbles along the way? Choosing the wrong path may lead to the witch's house.

Start

Finish

13

Finish

20,000 Leagues Under the Sea

Help Captain Nemo guide his submarine—the *Nautilus*—from the bottom of the sea to the surface. Watch out for the giant squid!

Start

Jack and the Beanstalk

Jack wants to grab the giant's magic harp—but
he has to climb the giant's shelves to get it!
Show him the way.

Start

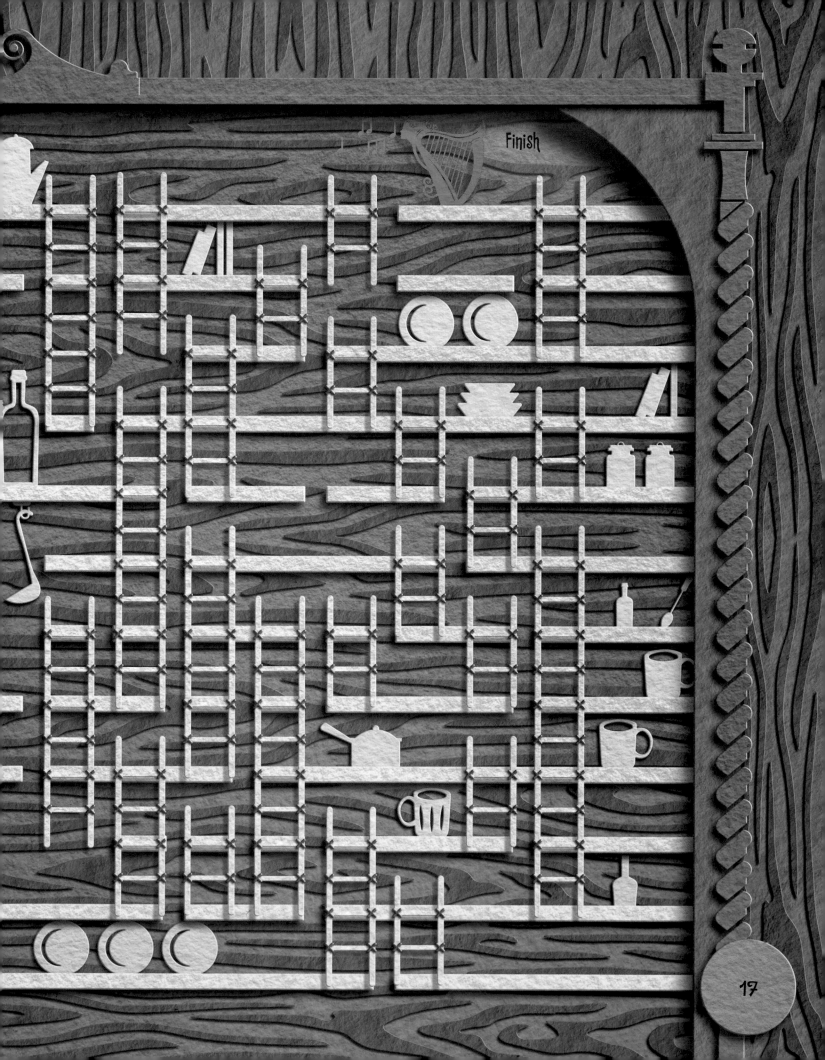

Finish

17

The Wonderful Wizard of Oz

A cyclone has sucked up the farmhouse—and Dorothy and her dog Toto are still inside! Guide them safely to the top of the cyclone, where the Munchkins await.

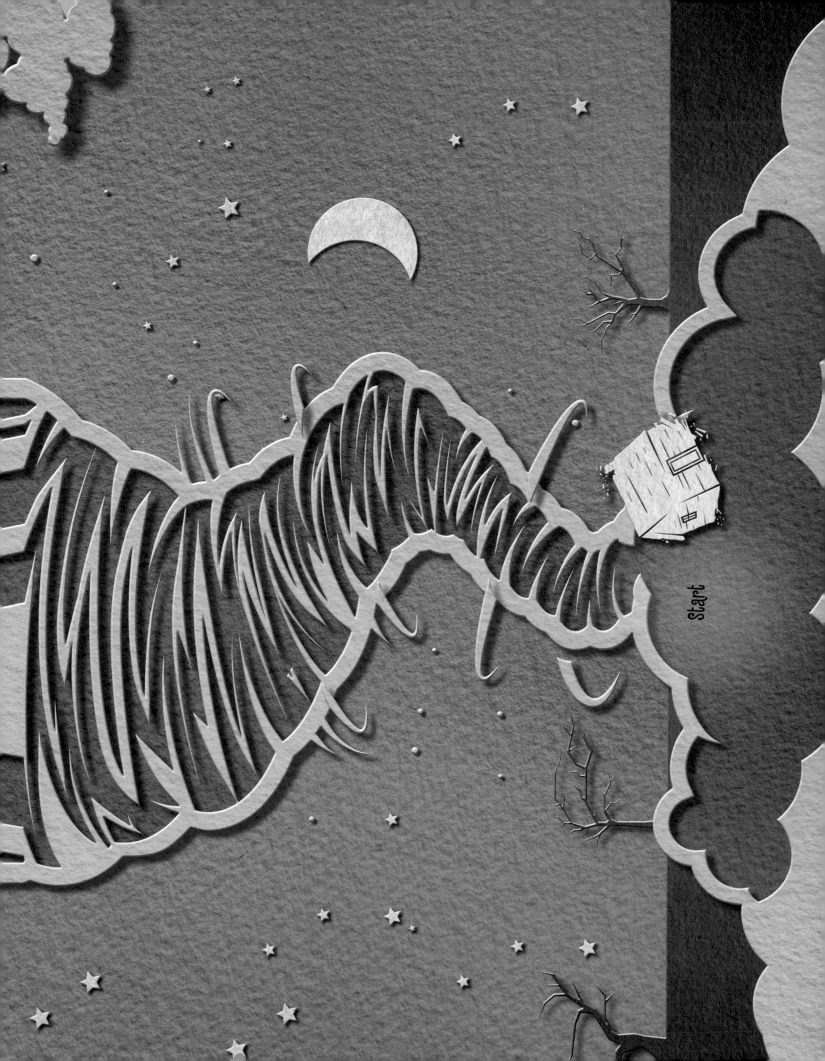

Start

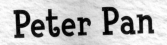

Peter Pan

"Second star to the right and straight on 'til morning."
Help Peter and Wendy fly through the night sky
to the island of Neverland. Be sure to meet
Peter's friend Tinker Bell along the way.

Start

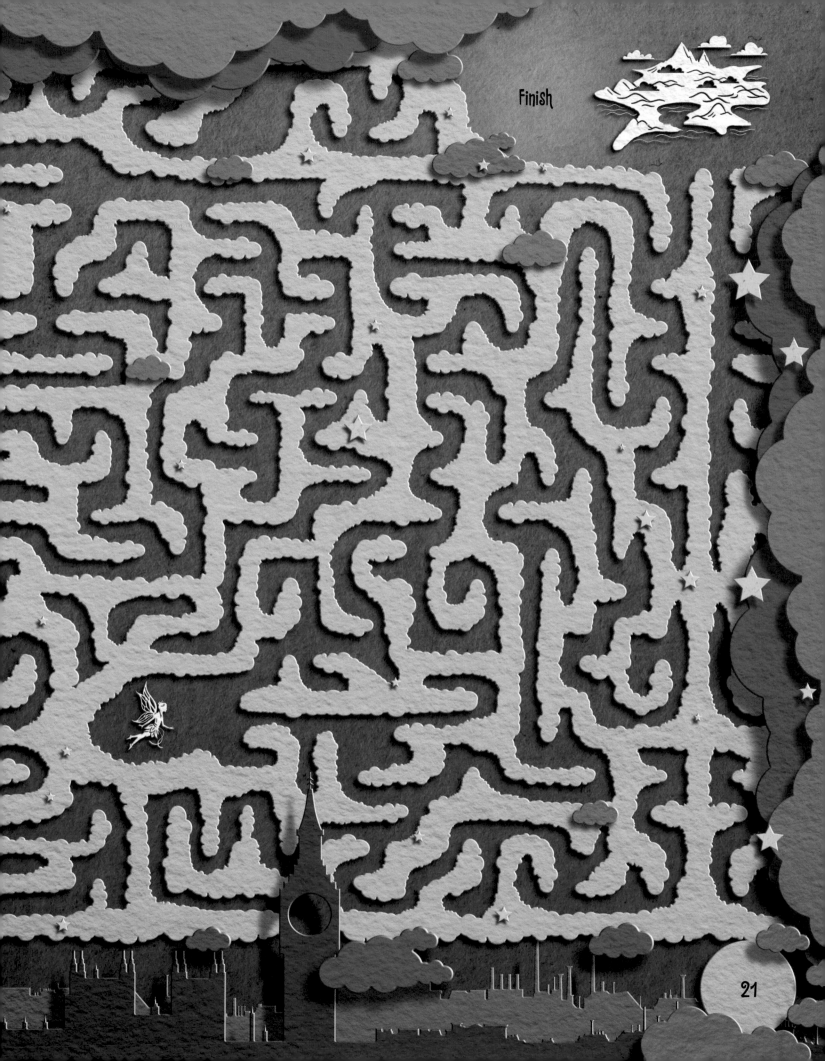

Finish

Gulliver's Travels

Gulliver has been tied down by the Lilliputians, but one of the tiny men has been left behind. Only one rope will help the Lilliputian climb over Gulliver and find his way home—which one is it?

Start

Finish

Cinderella

It's midnight and the ball has ended. Can you help the Prince find his way to Cinderella? Pick up the glass slipper along the way.

Start

Finish

Little Red Riding Hood

Help Little Red Riding Hood find her way
through the woods to Grandma's house.
Take care to avoid the Big Bad Wolf!

Start

Finish

27

The Adventures of Tom Sawyer

Help Tom and his friend Huckleberry Finn find the box of gold coins hidden in McDougal's Cave—but watch out for the skeleton!

Finish

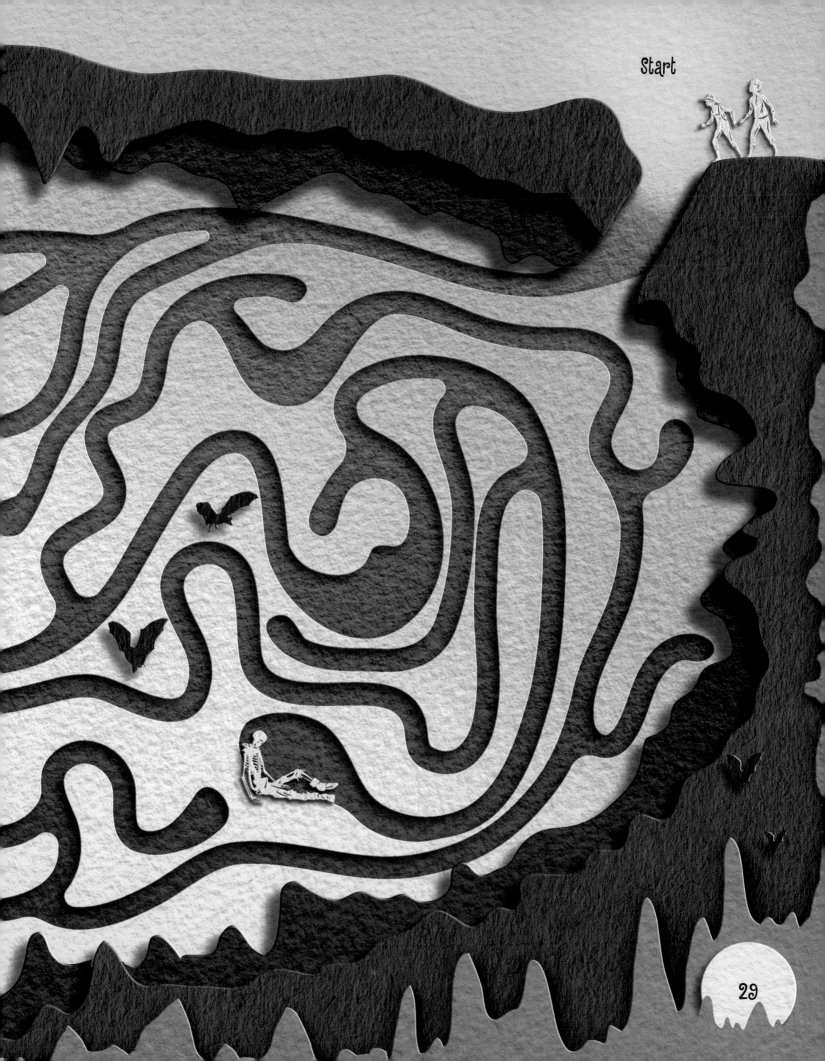

Start

29

The Secret Garden

"If you look the right way, you can see that the whole world is a garden." Show Mary how to get to the clearing in the secret garden, where her friend Dickon is waiting.

Start

Finish

The Adventures of Pinocchio

Pinocchio and Geppetto have been swallowed by the terrible Dogfish! Help them escape by showing them the way to the fish's open mouth.

Finish

Start

The Snow Queen

Gerda must find a way across the snowflakes to the Snow Queen's palace, where her friend Kai is imprisuned.

Finish

Start

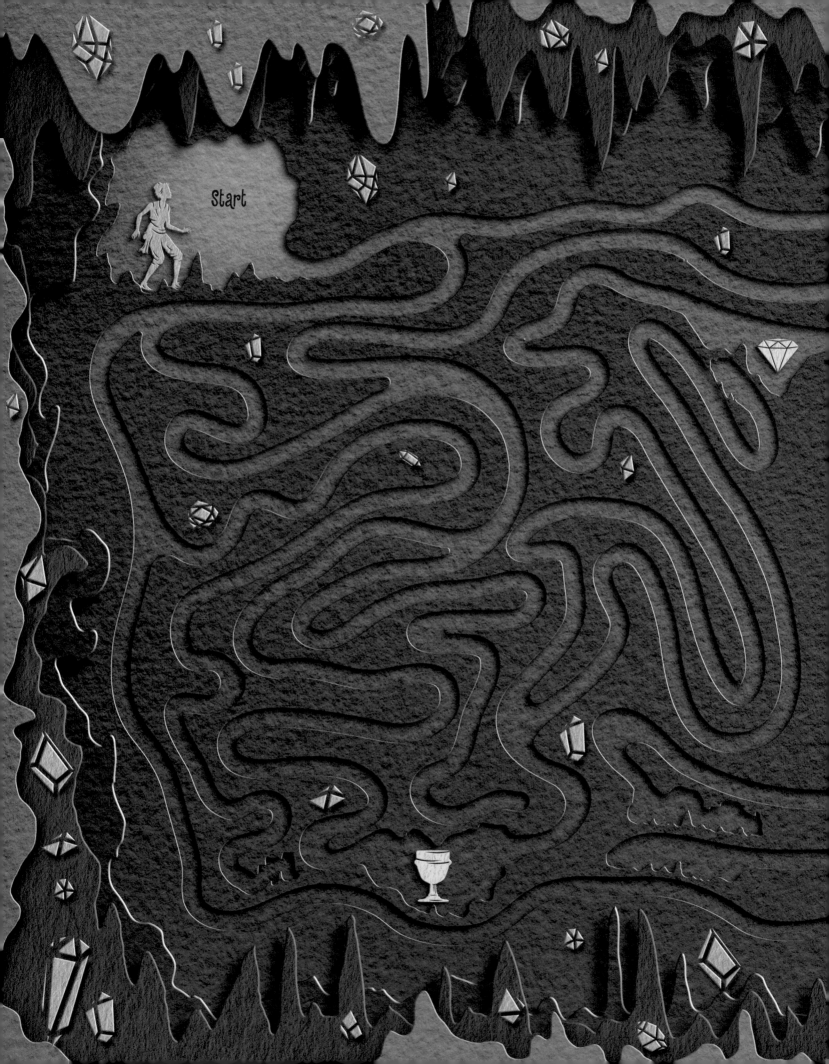

Start

Aladdin and the Magic Lamp

Help Aladdin find the magic lamp that is hidden in the secret cave. Collect three items of treasure along the way.

Finish

Robin Hood

Robin Hood wants to win the golden arrow prize and show the Sheriff of Nottingham that he's the best archer in the land. Which path should his arrow take to hit the middle of the target?

Start

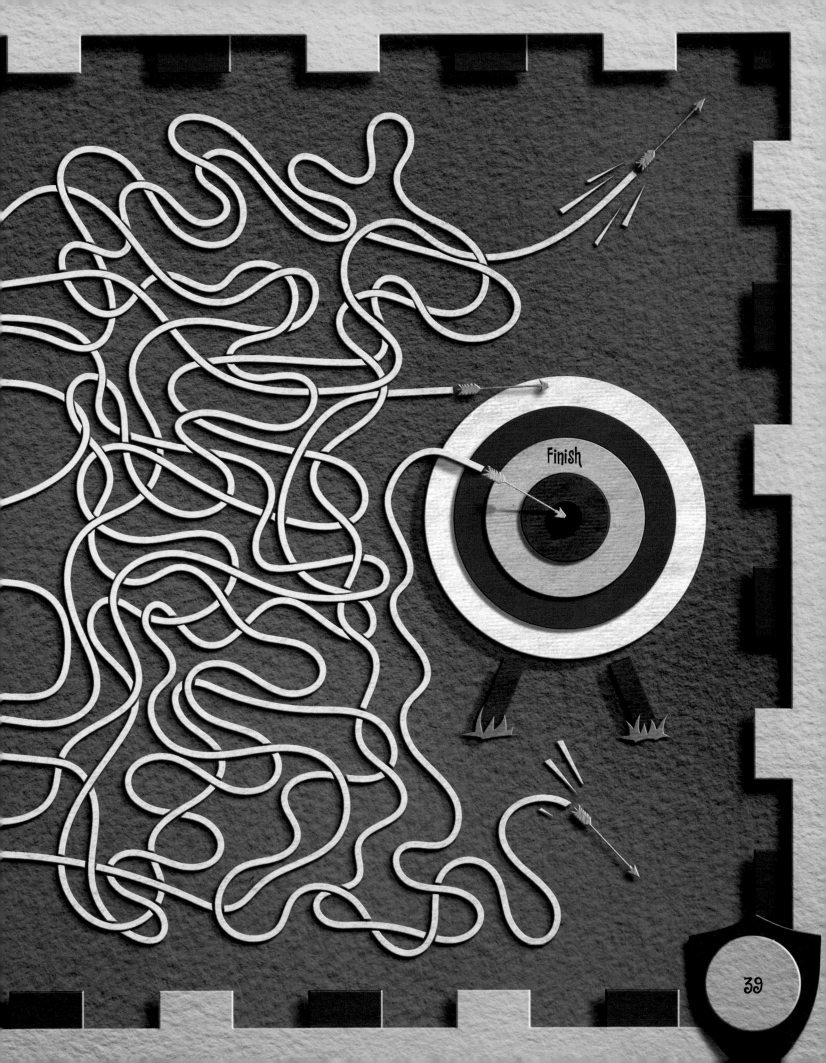

Finish

The Little Mermaid

The Little Mermaid must swim through the crashing waves to save the drowning Prince. Show her the way.

Finish

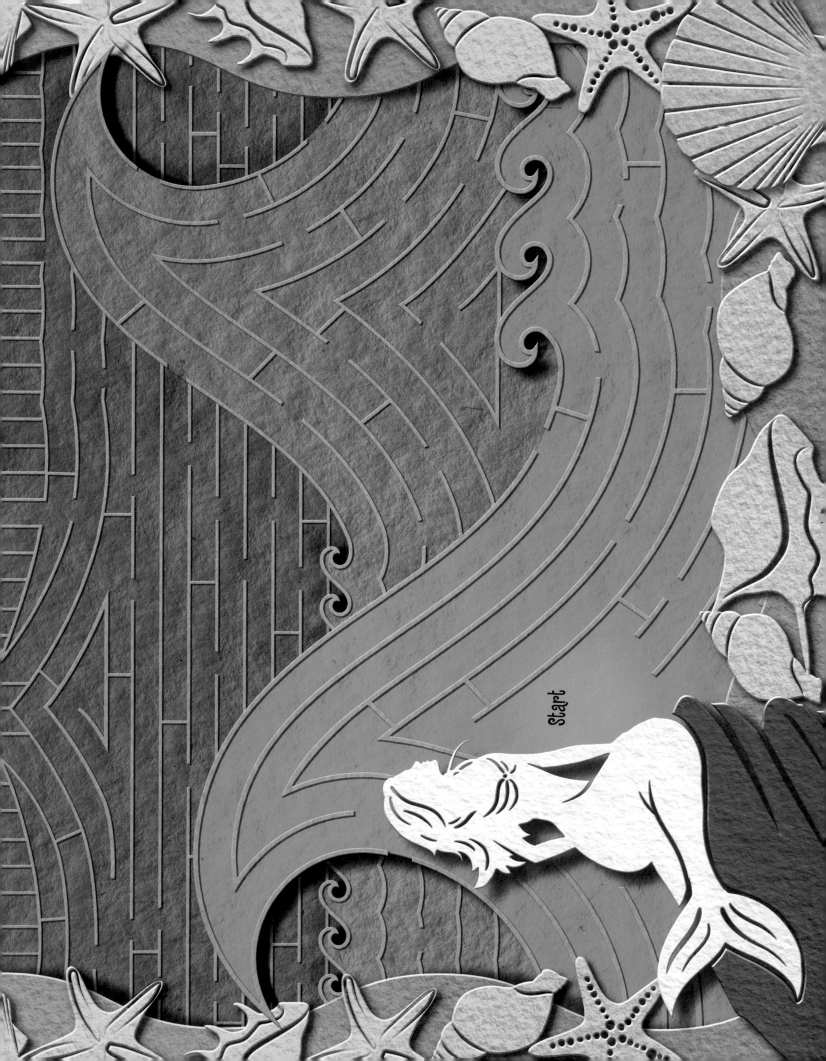

Start

Finish

The Wind in the Willows

The Weasels have taken over Toad Hall! Guide Badger through the secret underground tunnels so he can get to Toad Hall and scare away the intruders. Be sure to meet Ratty, Mole, and Toad along the way.

Start

The Jungle Book

Mowgli has been captured by monkeys! Help Baloo the bear find Mowgli and lead him out of the ruined temple, avoiding the monkeys along the way.

Finish

Start

Alice's Adventure's in Wonderland

Alice has shrunk and must swim through a pool of her own tears to reach dry land. Make sure she swims past Mouse along the way.

Start

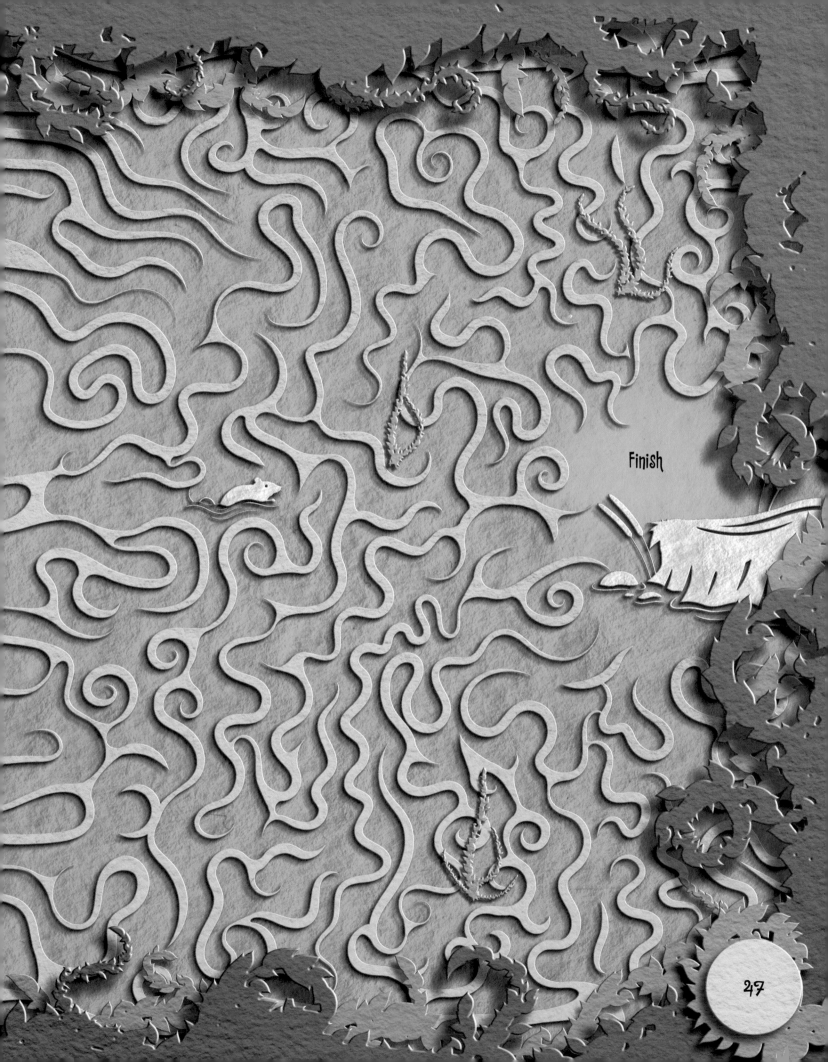

Finish

47

Aladdin and the Magic Lamp

The genie has just been released from the magic lamp. Only one plume of smoke leads from the lamp to the genie—can you find it?

Finish

Start

Jack and the Beanstalk

"Fee-fi-fo-fum!" The giant is chasing Jack down the beanstalk! Help Jack get home safely by showing him the way.

Start

Finish

Start

The Little Mermaid

Guide the Little Mermaid through the seaweed, so she can find the sea witch and ask her to turn her fish's tail into human legs.

Finish

The Wonderful Wizard of Oz

Help Dorothy and her pet dog Toto follow the Yellow Brick Road all the way to the Emerald City. She must meet her friends the Scarecrow, the Tin Woodman, and the Cowardly Lion along the way.

Start

Finish

Treasure Island

"Yo-ho-ho, and a bottle of rum!" Use this map to help Jim Hawkins find Captain Flint's treasure—but stay away from Long John Silver and his pirate pal!

Start

Finish

X

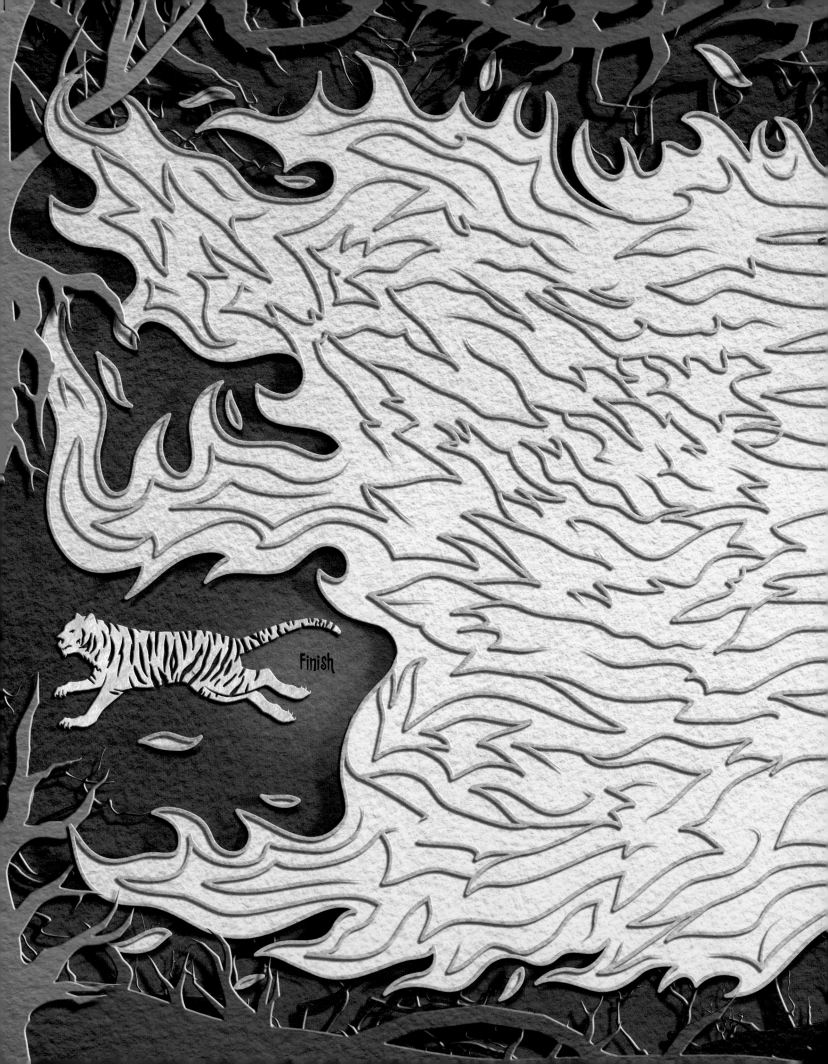

Finish

The Jungle Book

The tiger Shere Khan is scared of fire. Help Mowgli drive him out of the jungle by chasing him through the flames.

Start

SOLUTIONS

Pages 4-5

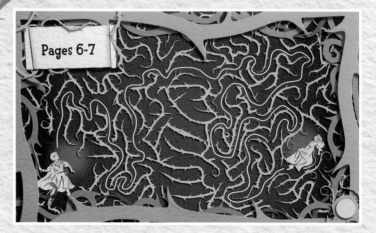

Pages 6-7

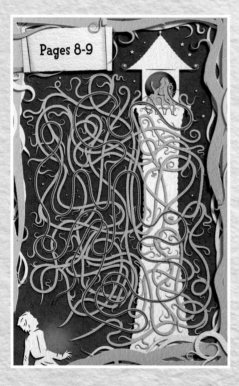

Pages 8-9

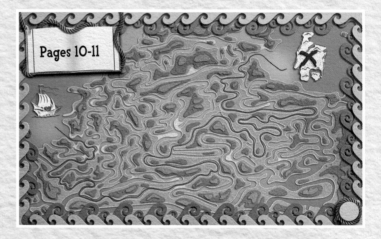

Pages 10-11

Pages 12-13

Pages 14-15

Pages 16-17

Pages 18-19

Pages 20-21

Pages 22-23

Pages 24-25

Pages 26-27

Pages 28-29

Pages 30-31

Pages 32-33

Pages 34-35

Pages 36-37

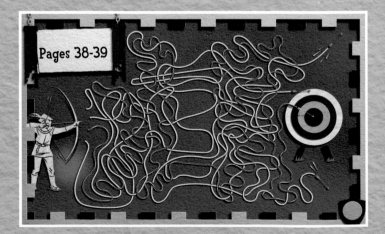
Pages 38-39

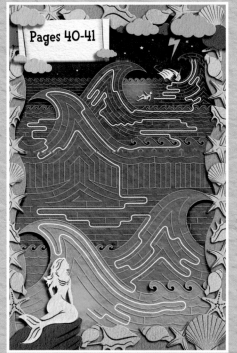

Pages 40-41

Pages 42-43

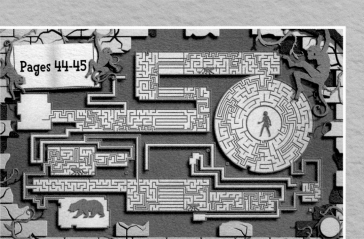

Pages 44-45

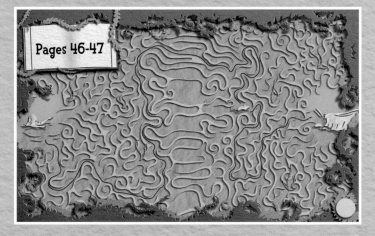

Pages 46-47

Pages 48-49

Pages 50-51

Pages 52-53

Pages 54-55

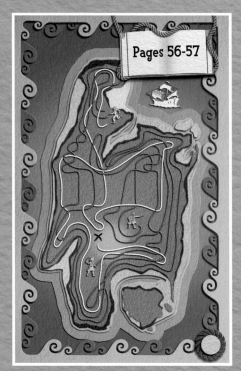

Pages 56-57

Pages 58-59